C000090172

Our senses tell us about the world around us. Our senses are:

| seeing | hearing | smelling | tasting | touching |

Under each picture write which sense is being used the most.

a _____

b _____

c _____

d _____

e _____

After most of the sentences, there are two words in brackets. Write the correct word in the space in the sentence.

f Our senses protect us from danger. If we want to cross the road, we _____ to see what is coming. **[look, feel]**

g Our _____ tell us if it is safe to cross. **[nose, eyes]**

h When a fire-engine is in a hurry, it sounds its _____. **[engine, siren]**

i Our _____ warn us the fire-engine is coming. **[ears, nose]**

j Our _____ may tell us that food is bad. **[ears, nose]**

k When we bite into an apple, our _____ may tell us it is sour. **[tongue, teeth]**

l Don't eat it or you'll get a _____ ache. **[head, tummy]**

m Is the dish in the oven too _____ to handle? **[hot, cold]**

n If you are silly and _____ it with your hand, you'll soon know. **[touch, grip]**

o Your _____ can tell you what is hot and what is cold. **[eyes, skin]**

Look at the pictures. They tell a story. The sentences below tell the same story, but the sentences are in the wrong order.
Write the sentences in the correct order.

a First she thanked him for handing in her purse.

He took it to the police station.

Then the woman gave Tim five pounds as a reward.

Tim found a purse in the street.

Two days later a woman called at Tim's house.

_____

_____

_____

_____

_____

b Questions end with a question mark. Write the conversation, using question marks or full stops where they are needed.

1st GIRL	Knock, knock
2nd GIRL	Who's there
1st GIRL	Ida
2nd GIRL	Ida Who
1st GIRL	Ida nidea you'd like to come out and play

_____

_____

_____

_____

Key Stage 2

Homework Book 2

For year 4

Schofield & Sims

HOMEWORK 2

thinking *writing*

Mathematics

science

"Language skills"

reading and vocabulary

Mathematics

Writing

"Language skills"

thinking

reading

and vocabulary

Name _____

A stag went to a pool to drink. The water acted as a mirror. The stag looked at his fine antlers. He said, "What a beautiful pair of antlers."
Then he saw his legs mirrored in the pool. The stag said, "How weak and thin my legs are. I wish they were as fine as my antlers." Just then a lion leapt at the stag. The stag ran for his life. The ground was free from trees. The stag's legs served him well. He drew ahead of the lion, and dashed into a forest.

The stag's antlers became tangled in the branches. He could not run and had to stop. The stag thought, "My legs served me well. But my antlers have let me down."
The lion leapt on the stag and killed him.

Complete these sentences.

a When the stag was at the pool, what did he most admire about himself? _____

b What displeased him? _____

c What leapt at the stag? _____

d On the open ground, which animal was the slower? _____

e When they reached the forest, which animal was ahead? _____

f In the forest, what became tangled in the branches? _____

g Why did the stag stop in the forest? _____

h In the forest, what did the lion do to the stag? _____

Mathematics 1

Write in the numbers on the clock faces.
Draw hands to show the time.

a half past 4

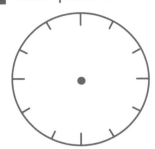

b a quarter to 8

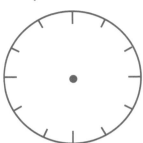

c a quarter past 12

Write each answer on the line.

d 9 + 7 + 3 = _____

e 12 + 3 − 5 = _____

f 17 − 8 = _____

g 15 − 4 + 8 = _____

h 5 x 5 = _____

i 6 x 4 = _____

j 3 x 7 = _____

k 6 x 5= _____

Fill in the blank coins.

l  are worth 75p

m  are worth 76p

n  are worth 53p

o are worth 96p

Put these words into alphabetical order.

a water   air   fire   soil   land

_____

b axe   ape   alien   airport   animal

_____

c body   bottle   bolt   boy   bonfire

_____

Each word below a picture ends with nd or nt.
Complete each word.

d    **e**    **f**    **g**

be ___   ha ___   wi ___   te ___

Make words by adding ng or n to each of the following.

h ri___   **i** ca___   **j** ma___   **k** ga___

l gu___   **m** lo___   **n** lu___   **o** fi___

Each day of the week needs one letter.
Finish the word by writing a letter in the space.

p M _ nday   **q** T _ esday   **r** We _ nesday

s Th _ rsday   **t** Fr _ day   **u** S _ turday

v S _ nday

Thinking 1

Let's think about the way things go together.
Here is an example.

Foot is to shoe as hand is to_____ .

The answer is **glove**. A shoe is worn on a foot, a glove is worn on a hand.

Write the word from the brackets that fits each blank.

a Boy is to girl as man is to_____ .   [person, adult, woman, human]

b Water is to thirst as food is to_____ .   [hunger, eat, dinner, snack]

c Day is to night as light is to_____ .   [black, dark, dawn, sunset]

d Dog is to puppy as cat is to_____ .   [friend, baby, tabby, kitten]

e Fish is to swim as bird is to _____ .   [run, fly, crawl, walk]

f Rifle is to bullet as bow is to_____ .   [arrow, feather, string, cannon]

g Roar is to lion as bark is to _____ .   [cough, dog, hunt, tree]

h Write in the value of the blank coins.

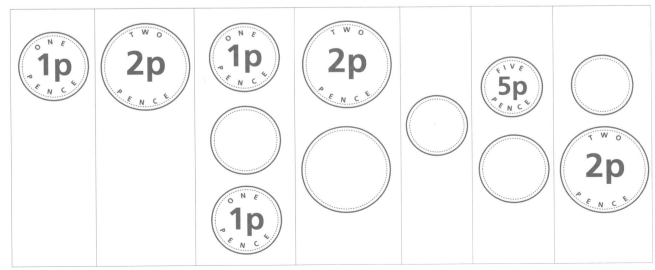

sneeze

yawn

shiver

Why do you sneeze, yawn and shiver?

When something gets into your nose, you sneeze. The rush of air pushes out whatever is irritating your nose.

You yawn when you feel tired. This gives you a deep breathe of air. The oxygen in the air helps your body to feel less tired.

Your muscles start to shiver when you are cold. By moving about they make some heat to keep you warm.

Your body sneezes, yawns and shivers to look after you.

Use a word from the list to complete each sentence.

cough	yawn	drink	cry
shiver	eat	sneeze	laugh

a We _____ to clear our throat.

b We _____ when we are tired.

c We _____ when we are hungry.

d We _____ when we are amused.

e We _____ when we are thirsty.

f We _____ when we are cold.

g We _____ when we are sad.

h We _____ to push out something irritating the inside of our noses.

Mathematics 2

Look at the prices in the picture. Write each answer in the space provided.

a An apple and a pear cost _____ p.

b Two bananas cost _____ p.

c An ice-cream and a chocolate bar cost _____ p.

d A banana and two apples cost _____ p.

e An apple, a pear and a banana cost _____ p.

f Two ice-creams cost _____ p.

g A chocolate bar and two apples cost _____ p.

h Three chocolate bars cost _____ p.

i Two pears and two bananas cost _____ p.

j A chocolate bar, an apple and a banana cost _____ p.

Count the marbles. Write the number of marbles in the first box. Make two equal shares. Write how many in each share in the double box.

		Number of marbles	Two equal shares	
k				
l				
m				
n				

a Write these names in alphabetical order.

Champion, Ahmed, Kenyon, Zaman, King, Aijaz, Chadwick, Kelly

1 _____ 2 _____ 3 _____ 4 _____

5 _____ 6 _____ 7 _____ 8 _____

b Look at each picture. Say its name to yourself.
Find the four pairs of names that rhyme.
Write the rhyming words in pairs.

_____ and _____

_____ and _____

_____ and _____

_____ and _____

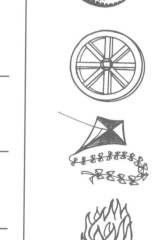

Each of the following needs two letters at the beginning to make
a word. Use one of the pairs of letters in brackets to complete
the word.

c ___ ash   [fl, bl]

d ___ one   [tr, st]

e ___ own   [pr, cr]

f ___ own   [cl, st]

g ___ oud   [dr, pr]

h ___ eep   [sl, sm]

Use a word from the list to fill each space.
Use each word only once.

iris	cry	under	light	dust	Eyes	brain
close	pupil	collects	Eyebrows	blinking	eyelid	

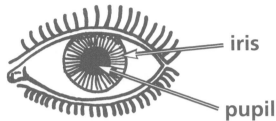

iris

pupil

a _____ are made to collect light.

b Our eyes tell our _____ what they see.

c The dark centre of the eye is called the_____.

d The pupil _____ the light.

e Round the pupil is the _____.

f In dull light the pupil gets bigger to collect as much _____ as possible.

g All day long we open and _____ our eyes very quickly.

h This is called _____.

i The _____ is like a wiper on a car window.

j Tears are made _____ the eyelid.

k When we _____ the tears spill out on our face.

l Eyelashes help to keep _____ out of our eyes.

m _____ stop sweat from going into our eyes.

Writing 2

An **abbreviation** is a shorter way of writing something.

Mr is an abbreviation of **Mister**.

Write each of these words in a shorter way.

a Street _____   **b** Avenue _____   **c** Road _____

d Doctor _____   **e** Captain _____   **f** Physical Education _____

g United Kingdom _____   **h** United States of America _____

i centimetre _____   **j** metre _____   **k** litre _____

l Write out this passage.

Put in the capital letters, full stops and question marks.

anne said, "my purse is missing have you seen it"
"no," said grant "when did you have it last"
"just before dinner," said anne "my shopping money is in there where can it be"
grant said, "have you looked in your shopping bag"
"no," replied anne
anne reached into her shopping bag she pulled out her purse
"thanks, grant," she said

_____

_____

_____

_____

_____

_____

_____

_____

Thinking 2

These pictures are all the same apart from one.
Write the number of the odd picture out in the box.

a

The odd picture out is [ ]

Fill in the missing numbers.

b 10 20 __ 40 50 60   **c** 80 60 __ 20

d __ 6 9 12 __ 18   **e** 3 13 __ 33 __ 53

f 1 2 4 5 __ 8 10 __   **g** 5 10 15 __ 25 __ 35

Which picture in each row is the odd one out?
Write the number of the picture.

h

The odd picture out is [ ]

i

   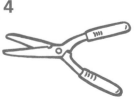

The odd picture out is [ ]

Three favourite summer fruits are strawberry, raspberry and blackcurrant.

| strawberry plant | raspberry canes | blackcurrant bush |

Strawberries grow on a low plant on the ground. Most of them are picked and eaten in June and July.

Next come the raspberries in July. They grow on canes about two metres high. The canes are grown up a frame made of posts and wires.

In August the blackcurrants are ripe and ready for picking. They grow on a bush about one metre high. The fruit grows in small bunches on a short stalk.

All three fruits can be eaten fresh, or made into jams or jellies. They are also used to flavour other foods, such as ice-cream and sweets.

Answer these questions.

a Which fruit grows on a bush? _____

b What do raspberries grow on? _____

c Which fruit is ready for picking first? _____

d Which fruit is grown up a frame? _____

e In which month are blackcurrants ready for picking?_____

Write each word in the list under the word with a similar meaning.

absurd	foolish
spiteful	unpleasant
silly	mean

f stupid

_____

_____

_____

g nasty

_____

_____

_____

HOMEWORK BOOK 2 ANSWERS

Note for users

Taking an interest in the child's work is of great importance. Take every opportunity to praise work that is correct, and offer help and advice where the child experiences difficulty. Make sure that the child understands the instructions which introduce each exercise. Some children experience more difficulty with the instructions than with the work itself.

There are advantages in allowing the child to mark his or her own work. This informs the child of the correct answer in cases where mistakes have occurred. It is important to look again at answers that are wrong and for the child to discover why an answer is incorrect so that he or she can learn as a result of the error.

Where a weakness is revealed, further similar exercises can be provided to give the child more practice and confidence.

A child should not be expected to undertake too much work in a short time. The exercises should be well spaced out so that the last pages are being worked towards the end of the appropriate school year.

Reading and Vocabulary 1

a his antlers b his legs c a lion
d the lion e the stag f his antlers
g his antlers h he killed the stag
   became tangled
   in the branches

Mathematics 1

a   b   c

d 19 e 10 f 9 g 19
h 25 i 24 j 21 k 30
l 5p m 1p n 10p o 20p

Language Skills 1

a air fire land soil water
b airport alien animal ape axe
c body bolt bonfire bottle boy
d bend e hand f wind
g tent h ring i can
j man k gang l gun
m long n lung o fin
p Monday q Tuesday r Wednesday
s Thursday t Friday u Saturday
v Sunday

Science 1

a hearing b smelling c touching
d seeing e tasting
f look g eyes h siren
i ears j nose k tongue
l tummy m hot n touch
o skin

Writing 1

a Tim found a purse in the street.
   He took it to the police station.
   Two dyas later a woman called at Tim's House
   First she thanked him for handing in her purse.
   Then the woman gave Tim five pounds as a reward.

b 1st GIRL: Knock, knock.
   2nd GIRL: Who's there?
   1st GIRL: Ida.
   2nd GIRL: Ida Who?
   1st GIRL: Ida nidea you'd like to come out and play.

Thinking 1

a woman b hunger c dark
d kitten e fly f arrow
g dog
h

Reading and Vocabulary 2

a cough b yawn c eat d laugh
e drink f shiver g cry h sneeze

Mathematics 2

a 20p b 22p c 50p d 27p
e 31p f 60p g 36p h 60p
i 46p j 39p

	Number of marbles	Two equal shares	
k	16	8	8
l	12	6	6
m	14	7	7
n	18	9	9

Language Skills 2

a Ahmed, Aijaz, Chadwick, Champion, Kelly, Kenyon,
   King, Zaman
b star and car   seal and wheel
   knight and kite tyre and fire
c flash d stone
e fly f clown
g proud h sleep

Science 2

a Eyes b brain c pupil
d collects e iris f light
g close h sleep i eyelid
j under k cry l dust
m Eyebrows

Writing 2

a	St	b	Ave	c	Rd	d	Dr
e	Capt	f	PE	g	UK	h	USA
i	cm	j	m	k	l		

l Anne said, "My purse is missing. Have you seen it?"
"No," said Grant. "When did you have it last?"
"Just before dinner," said Anne. "My shopping money is in there. Where can it be?"
Grant said, "Have you looked in your shopping bag?"
"No," replied Anne.
Anne reached into her shopping bag.
She pulled out her purse.
"Thanks, Grant," she said.

Thinking 2

a 3
b 30
c 40
d 3, 15
e 23, 43
f 7, 11
g 20, 30
h 3
i 1

Reading and Vocabulary 3

a	blackcurrant	b	canes
c	strawberry	d	raspberry
e	August		

f	stupid	g	nasty
	absurd		mean
	foolish		unpleasant
	silly		spiteful

Mathematics 3

a	7:00	b	2:30	c	11:15	d	12:00
e	6:30	f	4:15	g	10:00	h	3:30
i	14	j	16	k	30	l	18
m	96	n	June	o	24	p	a.m.
q	a.m.	r	a.m.	s	p.m.	t	p.m.
u	p.m.	v	p.m.	w	p.m.		

Language Skills 3

a	Ben	b	Pam	c	Joe	d	Kim
e	Lucy	f	Owen	g	Helen	h	Ryan
i	Yasmin						

j	trap	k	screw
	tray		octopus
	bray		radio
	pray		tractor
	play		heart
	plan		fish
			leaf
			girl
			egg
			kite
			hook

Science 3

a	F	b	T	c	T	d	F
e	T	f	T	g	F	h	T

Writing 3

a The first month of the year is January.
b My sister Helen will be five in April.
c The summer months are June, July and August.
d The day after Tuesday is Wednesday.
e We are going to London on the first Friday in March.
f My friend Andy is moving to Scotland in December.

g	Wed	h	31	i	Tue
j	November	k	September		

Thinking 3

a	angry	b	happy
c	afraid	d	sad
e	astray	f	solid	g	onlooker
h	today	i	nobody	j	inside

k I would wash my dirty hands with soap and water.
l I would drink the soup with a spoon.
m I would sweep up the broken vase with the dustpan and brush.
n I would ring/call the fire brigade on the telephone.

Reading and Vocabulary 4

a school   **b** tying   **c** milk
d upstairs/in her room   **e** ran   **f** holiday
g loser and winner   late and early
    seldom and often   laugh and cry

Mathematics 4

a 10	**b** 4	**c** 2	**d** 16
e 6	**f** 9	**g** 21	**h** 27
i yes	**j** 5	**k** 43	**l** 66
m 7	**n** 30	**o** 8	**p** 4
q l	**r** 2	**s** 3	**t** 4

u 5-11-98   **v** 23-8-97   **w** 1-1-99

Language Skills 4

a moon	**b** kite	**c** day
soon	right	ray
spoon	bite	bay
noon	flight	stay
June	night	clay

d cricket, football, hockey, netball, rugby, snooker, swimming, tennis

e doll	**f** pond	**g** bulb	**h** gift
i dress	**j** golf	**k** bell	**l** lamp

Science 4

a vibrates	**b** air	**c** all
d sound	**e** outer	**f** collected
g head	**h** eardrum	**i** middle
j shell	**k** bone	**l** liquid
m brain	**n** hears	

Writing 4

a		
inside	outside	shell
shed	grow	legs
large	catching	pools
nip	pick	crab
attract		

b kilometre   **c** Square
d Royal Air Force   **e** telephone
f Roman Catholic   **g** television

Thinking 4

a 7:15 a.m., 11:30 a.m., 3:15 p.m., 7:45 p.m.
b apple   **c** pale   **d** sleep
e Sun   **f** carrot   **g** ball
h 3, 1, 4, 2

Reading and Vocabulary 5

a packs	Earth	animal
men	other	friends
jobs	greyhound	are
used	wild	bones
sleeping	dog	

b happy – glad, merry, carefree, pleased, cheerful, delighted

c miserable – dejected, gloomy, unhappy, depressed, sad, wretched

Mathematics 5

a yes	**b** no	**c** 50
d 200	**e** yes	**f** 150
g 50p	**h** 20p	**i** 5p
j 10p	**k** 54	**l** 58
m 68	**n** 68	**o** 88
p 99	**q** 94	**r** 99
s 89	**t** 78	

Write these times on the digital clocks.

a 7 o'clock

[:   ]

b 2 thirty

[:   ]

c 11 fifteen

[:   ]

d 12 o'clock

[:   ]

e 6 thirty

[:   ]

f 4 fifteen

[:   ]

g 10 o'clock

[:   ]

h 3 thirty

[:   ]

Write each answer on the line.

i How many days in two weeks? _____

j How many shoes in eight pairs? _____

k How many days in April? _____

l Two times nine is? _____

m What is ninety plus six? _____

n What is the sixth month of the year? _____

o How many hours are there in a whole day? _____

The hours from midnight to midday are called **a.m.**
The hours from midday to midnight are called **p.m.**

Circle a.m. or p.m. on each line.

p Kirsty gets up at 7:30 a.m. / p.m.

q She has breakfast at 8:15 a.m. / p.m.

r School begins at 9:00 a.m. / p.m.

s Kirsty leaves school at 3:30 a.m. / p.m.

t Kirsty watches television at 4:00 a.m. / p.m.

u The evening meal is at 6:30 a.m. / p.m.

v Bedtime is at 8:00 a.m. / p.m.

w Kirsty reads in bed for a while,
but is usually asleep by 8:30 a.m. / p.m.

Language Skills 3

Fill in the missing vowels to make these first names.

a B __ n

b P __ m

c J __ e

d K __ m

e L __ cy

f Ow __ n

g H __ l __ n

h Ry __ n

i Y __ sm __ n

j Begin with the top word. Change one letter to make the word shown in the next picture. And so on.

k The last letter of one word becomes the first letter of the next word.

All the words you need are shown as pictures.

Climb the ladder.

trap

k

hook

Science 3

Read the passage.

There are different kinds of eyes.
Our eyes are at the front of our heads.
This helps us to know how far things
are ahead of us.

Animals that hunt have eyes at the
front of their heads. Other animals

have eyes at the sides of their heads. These animals can see two pictures, one on

each side of them. They can also see a little to the
front and a little to the back. Eyes at the side can help
animals that are hunted. They can see what is
happening all around them.

Have you seen a cat's eyes glow when a light shines
on them? That is because they have a kind of small
mirror inside their eyes. It collects all the light there
is. They can see well when it is almost dark. This
helps animals that hunt at night.

Read each sentence. Write 'T' if it is True, and 'F' it it is False.

a All animals have eyes at the front of their heads. ⎯⎯⎯

b Many animals that are hunted have eyes at the sides of their heads. ⎯⎯⎯

c Eyes at the sides of the head can help an animal to see all around it. ⎯⎯⎯

d Our eyes help us to see what is behind us. ⎯⎯⎯

e An animal with eyes at the sides of the head can see two pictures,
one on each side of it. ⎯⎯⎯

f Lions and tigers have eyes at the front of their heads. ⎯⎯⎯

g The kind of small mirror in a cat's eye helps it to see all around it. ⎯⎯⎯

h Cats can see well when it is almost dark because the small mirrors
in their eyes collect all the light there is. ⎯⎯⎯

Writing 3

Days of the week and months of the year begin with a capital letter.

October						
Sun	Mon	Tue	Wed	Thu	Fri	Sat
		1	2	3	4	5
6	7	8	9	10	11	12
13	14	15	16	17	18	19
20	21	22	23	24	25	26
27	28	29	30	31		

Write out each sentence, using capital letters and full stops where they are needed.

a the first month of the year is january

_____

b my sister helen will be five in april

_____

c the summer months are june, july and august

_____

d the day after tuesday is wednesday

_____

e we are going to london on the first friday in march

_____

f my friend andy is moving to scotland in december

_____

Fill in the blanks.

g The abbreviation for Wednesday is_____.

h There are_____ days in October.

i The abbreviation for Tuesday is_____.

j The month after October is_____.

k The month before October is_____.

Which word describes how the girl in each picture feels?
Write a word from the list below each picture.

| happy | sad | angry | afraid |

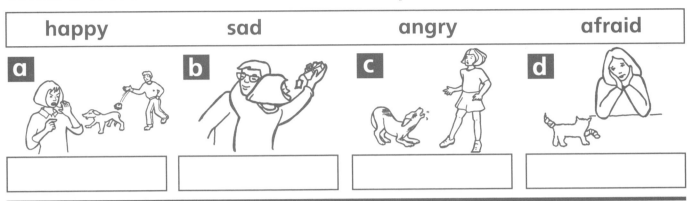

Which two-letter word from the list could you put in front of each of the words below to make six new words?
Write each new word on the line.

| on | to | no | as | so | in |

e tray ➡ _____

f lid ➡ _____

g looker ➡ _____

h day ➡ _____

i body ➡ _____

j side ➡ _____

What would you use from the second line of pictures to deal with what is happening in the first line of pictures?
Finish the sentences after the pictures?

telephone   soap   spoon   dustpan and brush

k I would wash my dirty _____ with _____ and water.

l I would _____ the _____ with a spoon.

m I would sweep up the broken vase with_____and _____.

n I would _____ the fire brigade on the _____.

Ruth got out of bed late. She dashed about, bumping into people and things.
"Tie your shoelace," said Mum
The shoelace broke. "Find another. That clock's slow," said Mum. "You'll be late for school. Hurry up and eat your breakfast."
At the table, Ruth knocked over the milk. Ruth's baby brother began to cry. Ruth left the table and stood on the cat.
"My school bag," shouted Ruth, "where's my school bag?"
"You took it to your room," said Mum. Ruth dashed upstairs. She tripped coming down, and dropped the bag. It opened and books flew all over the place. Ruth packed them back in the bag again. She dashed to the front door.
"Bye, Mum."
"Bye, Ruth."
It was a short walk to school, but Ruth ran. The gate was closed. There was no one about.
Then Ruth remembered. It was a school holiday!

Complete the sentences.

a Ruth was afraid she would be late for _____.

b Her shoelace broke when she was _____ it up.

c The baby began crying when Ruth knocked over the _____.

d Ruth had left her school bag _____.

e She _____ to school.

f No one was there because it was a school_____.

The words **up** and **down** have opposite meanings.
Write down the four pairs of opposites from the word list.

loser	late	laugh	often	seldom	cry	winner	early

g _____ and _____   _____ and _____

_____ and _____   _____ and _____

Mathematics 4

Write each answer on the line.

a 2 x 5 = _____   **b** 2 x 2 = _____   **c** 1 x 2 = _____   **d** 2 x 8 = _____

e 3 x 2 = _____   **f** 3 x 3 = _____   **g** 3 x 7 = _____   **h** 3 x 9 = _____

i Is 3 x 2 the same as 2 x 3? _____

j How many tens in 57? _____

k Forty plus three is _____

l 6 tens and 6 ones make _____

m Take 9 from 16 _____

n Double 15 is _____

o 19 = _____ plus 11

p Subtract 8 from 12 _____

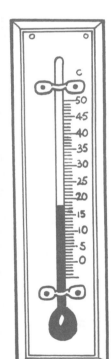

Look at the thermometer on the left. It tells us how hot or cold it is. It shows that the temperature is 18 degrees Celsius.

The short way to write this is 18°C.

Look at the four small thermometers and answer the questions.

 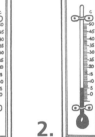  

1.   2.   3.   4.

q Which thermometer shows the highest temperature? _____

r Which shows the lowest temperature? _____

s Which thermometer shows 10°C? _____

t Which thermometer shows 15°C? _____

The date can be written in different ways.
The long way: 17 March, 1997. The short way: 17-3-97.
Write these dates the short way.

u 5 November, 1998 _____

v 23 August, 1997 _____

w 1 January, 1999 _____

Language Skills 4

Use the words in the panel to make three lists of words that rhyme.
The words in each list must rhyme with the word at the top.

right	ray	bay	bite	soon	flight
stay	spoon	noon	clay	night	June

a moon

_____

_____

_____

_____

b kite

_____

_____

_____

_____

c day

_____

_____

_____

_____

d Write the names of these sports in alphabetical order.

football   netball   rugby   tennis
cricket   snooker   hockey   swimming

1 _____   2 _____   3 _____   4 _____

5 _____   6 _____   7 _____   8 _____

Write two letters below each picture to complete the word.

e do ___

f po ___

g bu ___

h gi ___

i dre ___

j go ___

k be ___

l la ___

Science 4

After most of the sentences there are two words in brackets.
Write the correct word in the space in the sentence.

a Sounds are vibrations. If you stretch a rubber band and pull it,
it _____ . **[vibrates/records]**

b This vibrates the _____ around it. **[rubber/air]**

c The vibrations travel in _____ directions. **[some/all]**

d We call these vibrations _____ waves. **[sound/light]**

MIDDLE EAR

INNER EAR

SOUND WAVES

TO THE BRAIN

EARDRUM

OUTER EAR

e Look at the picture. The _____ ear is the only part of the ear that
can be seen from outside. **[middle/outer]**

f Sound waves are _____ by the outer ear. **[made/collected]**

g The sound waves go into a tube which goes into the _____.
[brain/head]

h The waves vibrate the _____ at the end of the tube. **[eardrum/hairs]**

i Three tiny bones take the vibrations through the _____ ear.
[outer/middle]

j Then the vibrations go into a hollow bone, which is shaped like a snail's
_____ . **[body/shell]**

k A liquid in this _____ is moved by the vibrations. **[bone/shell]**

l The moving _____ touches the ends of nerves in the bone.
[bone/liquid]

m The nerves then carry the sound vibrations to the _____ . **[brain/ear]**

n That is how our brains _____ a sound. **[hear/make]**

Writing 4

Put one word from the list in each space in the passage.

large	pick	pools	catching	inside	attract
grow	outside	shed	nip	legs	crab	shell

shore crab

fiddler crab

a Humans have a skeleton _____ their bodies.

But crabs have their skeleton on the _____. This is their

_____ . As they grow, crabs _____ their shells, and

_____ new ones. Crabs have five pairs of _____.

The front pair are _____ claws. They use these for fighting and

_____ food.

The shore crab lives in rock _____ and on the beach. It may

_____ you with its claws if you try to _____ it up.

The male fiddler _____ has one huge claw which is often

brightly coloured. It uses this to _____ female crabs or to defend

its territory.

Write these abbreviations in full.

b km _____

c Sq _____

d RAF _____

e tel _____

f RC _____

g telly _____

Thinking 4

The first digital clock is in its correct place. The other clocks are not in their time order.
Arrange them in their time order in the blank clocks.

| 7:45 a.m. | 7:15 p.m. | 3:15 p.m. | 11:30 a.m. |

a

| | | | |

Write the word which does not belong.

b rain   snow   hail   apple   _____

c red   pale   green   yellow   _____

d run   jump   sleep   walk   _____

e Venus   Sun   Mars   Earth   _____

f carrot   pear   plum   banana   _____

g football   rugby   tennis   ball   _____

---

h The pictures are in the wrong order.
Write the numbers of the pictures in their correct order.

1   2   3   4

_____   _____   _____   _____

Reading and Vocabulary 5

jobs	friends	men	bones	dog	packs	greyhound
other	Earth	wild	are	used	animal	sleeping

Use a word from the list to fill the spaces.

a Wild dogs hunted in _____ long before there were people on
_____ . The dog was the first _____ to be tamed by people.
Dogs hunted with _____ . They also helped men to herd_____
animals. People were glad to have dogs as _____ .

Dogs were bred to do certain _____ .
The _____ was bred for racing.
Dogs _____ trained for police work.
Dogs are also _____ to guide the blind.

Pet dogs have not lost all their_____ ways.
They bury _____, as they did when they were wild.
They turn round to look for enemies before _____ .

The _____ is often called man's best friend.

Use the words from the box to make lists of words similar to <u>happy</u> and <u>miserable.</u>

glad	dejected	gloomy	merry	carefree	unhappy
depressed	pleased	sad	cheerful	wretched	delighted

b happy _____ _____ _____

_____ _____ _____

c miserable _____ _____ _____

_____ _____ _____

Mathematics 5

There are 100 centimetres in a metre. (1 m = 100 cm)
Answer these questions.

a Is your front door taller then one metre? _____

b Is your pen or pencil a metre long? _____

c How many centimetres in half a metre? _____

d How many centimetres in two metres? _____

e Is your bed longer than a metre? _____

f How many centimetres in one-and-a-half metres? _____

Make each line of coins worth £1 by filling in the blank coin.

g 50p ( ) = £1

h 50p 20p ( ) 10p = £1

i 50p 20p 10p 10p ( ) 5p = £1

j 20p 20p 20p 20p ( ) 5p 5p = £1

Write each answer on the dotted line.

k   33
     + 21
     ----

l   23
     + 35
     ----

m   36
     + 32
     ----

n   41
     + 27
     ----

o   56
     + 32
     ----

p   16
     + 83
     ----

q   73
     + 21
     ----

r   92
     + 7
     ----

s   76
     + 13
     ----

t   62
     + 16

Schofield & Sims
HELPING CHILDREN TO LEARN

Schofield & Sims was established in 1901 by two headmasters and since then our name has been synonymous with educationally sound texts and teaching materials. Our mission is to publish products which are:

- **Educationally sound • Good value • Written by experienced teachers**
- **Extensively used in schools, nurseries and play groups**
- **Used by parents to support their children's learning**

HOMEWORK 2

Exercises in reading and vocabulary, language skills, writing, mathematics, science and thinking. Suitable for use at home, with or without parental help. Each book includes an answer book.

Homework Book 1 - 0 7217 0845 5

Homework Book 2 - 0 7217 0846 3

Homework Book 3 - 0 7217 0851 X

Homework Book 4 - 0 7217 0852 8

Schofield & Sims Key Stage 2 products for 7 to 11 year olds

Language and literacy workbooks

Key Spellings

Books 1 - 4

Pattern and sound based spelling activities and exercises to establish basic spelling skills.

New Spellaway

Books 1 - 4

A progressive series complementing the formal teaching of spelling. New patterns are consolidated, through the 'look, say, cover, write, check' approach.

Springboard

Books 1 - 8 plus Introductory Book

English workbooks covering word construction, spelling, vocabulary, grammar, comprehension exercises and creative work. Age range 6 - 11.

Maths and numeracy workbooks

Mental Arithmetic

Books 1 - 6 plus Introductory Book

Covers essential mental maths skills through 36 carefully graded tests in each book along with progress tests and diagnostic tests. Supported by corresponding series of Teacher's Books.

Times Tables

Books 1 and 2

Straight forward tables practice.

Book 2 covers x6, x7, x8, x9, x11, x12 tables. (Book 1 is for Key Stage 1)

Posters

Sturdy laminated posters, full colour, write-on/wipe-off, suitable for wall mounting or desk top use. Over 70 titles covering numeracy, literacy, science, nature, geography, history and languages.

Information

For further information about products for pre-school, Key Stages 1 and 2, please request our catalogue or visit our website at **www.schofieldandsims.co.uk**

Author   Chris Burgess

Cover design   Curve Creative - Bradford

©1997 Schofield & Sims Ltd.

First printed 1998

Reprinted 1998 (twice), 1999 (three times), 2000 2001 (twice), 2002, 2003

Printed by Hawthornes Printers, Nottingham

Schofield & Sims

Dogley Mill, Fenay Bridge, Huddersfield, HD8 0NQ
Phone 01484 607080   Fax 01484 606815
e-mail sales@schofieldandsims.co.uk

ISBN 0-7217-0846-3

9 780721 708461

Price £1.95

Key Stage 2

Age Range 7-11 years